LARGE MAIN FRAME CO[...] P9-DFP-778

A MICRO COMPUTER

If you are interested in computers, their function and operation, but are discouraged by their complexity, you should read this book. It deals as simply as possible with the principles and does not delve too deeply into electronics. The combination of carefully-written text and instructive illustrations should give older students a good basic knowledge of what computers are all about.

The new printing technology has been applied with the Monotype 'Lasercomp' to set the text in this book. The 'Lasercomp' is an advanced computer controlled high-speed photosetter which uses digitised characters, and a laser light beam for character definition. It is the only system of its kind in the world.

Acknowledgments

The publishers wish to acknowledge the help of
R S Edwards of Rika Computer Systems Ltd and
D R Noaks B Sc, C Eng when preparing this book.
Photographs and reference material were also
supplied by Allied Business Systems Ltd; Burroughs
Machines Ltd; Data Communications Corporation;
Digital Equipment Co Ltd; Hewlett Packard Ltd;
IBM United Kingdom Ltd; and International
Computers Ltd.

HOW IT WORKS...
THE COMPUTER

by DAVID CAREY
New material in this edition
prepared by JAMES BLYTHE
with illustrations by B H ROBINSON
and GERALD WITCOMB MSIAD

Ladybird Books
Loughborough

What are Computers?

There is something about computers that is both fascinating and intimidating. They are fascinating when they are used in rocketry and space research, and when they enable man to get to the moon and back. Many people think of them as almost-human machines with 'brains' that allow them to think. After all, there are computers which play 'music' or 'speak'. On the other hand, we are inclined to be intimidated by their complex mechanisms and the involved scientific principles upon which they are built.

In fact, computers do not have brains and they cannot really think for themselves. They are primarily machines for doing arithmetic. They are automatically controlled and do the work of many human beings at fantastically high speeds. The really important thinking is done by the humans who feed them with information and *program* them to perform particular operations with the information they are given.

Although primarily a calculating machine, the modern computer can also store up a vast mass of information. It can be programmed to carry out 'logical' operations, such as transferring certain information from one part of the machine to another, sorting this information and comparing it with other pieces of information or using it in arithmetical calculations. We hope this book will help you to understand how most of this is done.

PROGRAM LISTING

```
MOVE -1 TO CUST-USE-FLAG.
WRITE CUSTREC INVALID KEY GO TO DELETION-ERROR.
ADD 1 TO RECADD, RECCNT.
DISPLAY "RECORD DELETED " TRANSCUST.
GO TO REQUEST-DETS.
DELION-ERROR.
    ADD 1 TO RECREJ.
    ADD 1 TO RECCNT.
    DISPLAY "DELETION ERROR", GO TO REQUEST-DETS.
INQUIRE-FUNCTION.
    IF TRANSCUST NOT NUMERIC OR TRANSCUST EQUAL ZERO
    MOVE ZERO TO RCT-CUST-KEY.
    MOVE TRANSCUST TO CUST-KEY.
    READ CUSTOMER INVALID KEY GO TO REC-NOT-FOUND.
    ADD 1 TO RECENY, RECCNT.
    MOVE SPACES TO SCREEN-C-NAME.
    MOVE SPACES TO SCREEN-C-L1, SCREEN-C-L2.
    MOVE SPACES TO SCREEN-C-L4, SCREEN-C-L4.
    MOVE ZEROS TO SCREEN-C-ADD, SCREEN-C-BAL.
    MOVE ZEROS TO SCREEN-C-STAT, SCREEN-C-DATE.
    MOVE CUST-NO TO SCREEN-C-NO.
    MOVE CUST-NAME TO SCREEN-C-NAME.
    MOVE CUST-ADD-L1 TO SCREEN-C-L1.
    MOVE CUST-ADD-L2 TO SCREEN-C-L2.
    MOVE CUST-ADD-L3 TO SCREEN-C-L3.
    MOVE CUST-ADD-L4 TO SCREEN-C-L4.
    MOVE CUST-BAL TO SCREEN-C-BAL.
    MOVE CUST-NO TO SCREEN-C-NO.
    MOVE CUST-ADD-DATE TO SCREEN-C-DATE.
    DISPLAY " ". DISPLAY " ".
```

PRINTED CIRCUIT BOARD

MINI COMPUTER CONTROL UNIT

How Computers Developed

To think that computers have suddenly arrived on the scene would be wrong, although it is true that their number and use have greatly increased during recent years. Desk calculators have been in use for a very long time, and even in the days of the old navigators and astronomers there was a need for some sort of calculating instrument to relieve the human brain of work.

The first mechanical calculator was produced by Blaise Pascal in 1642. Others tried to improve on it but not until the nineteenth century was any real progress made. In 1801 a Frenchman named Jacquard invented a punched card system for controlling the threads on his weaving looms. Charles Babbage followed in 1833 with his 'Analytical Engine', which could perform calculations automatically, using punched cards. This was the first *digital* computer (a machine that performs calculations with numbers). The American Hollerith system also used punched cards, but the calculating machinery was operated by electromagnetic means. It was introduced in 1889 and was generally used in a highly developed form right up to the widespread introduction of electronic computers in the 1950s.

1943 saw the need for computing artillery firing charts, and ENIAC (Electronic Numerical Integrator and Calculator) was born. EDSAC (Electronic Delay Storage Automatic Calculator) was first used at Cambridge University six years later. And so the modern electronic computer came into being.

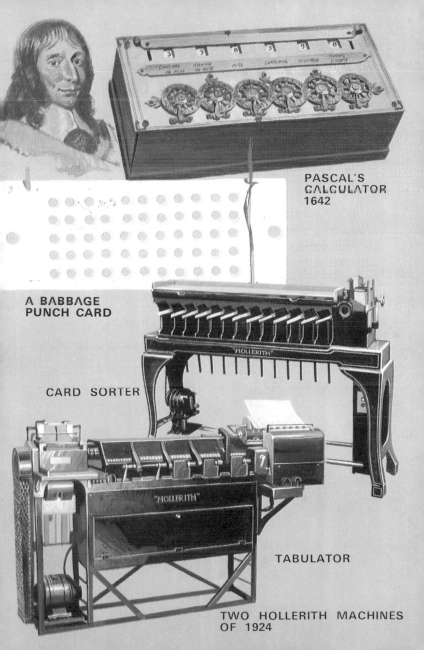

PASCAL'S CALCULATOR 1642

A BABBAGE PUNCH CARD

CARD SORTER

TABULATOR

TWO HOLLERITH MACHINES OF 1924

Different Designs

The name computer covers many different types of machine. Early electronic computers were developed around valves, which were large and gave off a lot of heat. Later transistors were used. Continued miniaturization of components allowed smaller and smaller computers to be made, but also allowed the power of computers to increase rapidly. Manned space flights needed a small computer that gave an instant response to many sources of information, whilst also calculating complex mathematical equations. The computer used in this project became known as the mini computer. Development of these mini computers continued alongside the development of the main frame computer. Nowadays we are constantly using even smaller computers (micro computers) in everyday life. Micro computers control washing machines, watches, cash tills, and help in the servicing of cars. They are also used in offices to calculate accounts, wages and other office needs.

As computers became smaller and more powerful so their uses developed within science, technology and business.

Computers are sometimes designed for a particular purpose, so each type of machine has its own variations, depending on the work it will have to do. Machines handling data for scientific work, for industry or for commercial undertakings, all have their own special features. In the following pages we will consider what we might loosely call a typical electronic digital computer system with its subsidiary equipment for receiving, storing and presenting information.

MAIN FRAME COMPUTER INSTALLATION

MINI COMPUTER SYSTEM

Data Processing

As we have already mentioned, there are a great many kinds of computers, some being designed for a particular purpose. Our 'typical' machine will very likely be used for 'data processing' in a large manufacturing organisation in which there will be a great amount of routine office work. For instance, the pay-roll has to be prepared every week and the names and wages of all the employees printed on their individual pay slips. Records of all the employees must be maintained and continually brought up to date as some people leave and others are engaged.

This computer may also be used to calculate the amount of material of different kinds that will be needed in factory production, and thus help to bring the hundreds of parts forward to the assembly line in the right sequence and at the right time. Records of sales of different products can be kept and forecasts made of possible future sales.

An organisation would use a computer only if by so doing it is more profitable. This profitability might be related either to increase in production or to reduction of wastage. The introduction of a computer rarely decreases a labour force. It is more likely, due to the increase in production, to expand labour requirements within parts of the organisation.

Space Travel

Navigation

Banking

Traffic Control

Power

Meteorology

Air Travel

Medicine

Industry

Printing

Telephone and Telex

Police

The Main Parts of a Computer

A computer system consists of a number of different units each of which has its own special function.

Central Processing Unit (CPU)

1 *Control Unit*
   All the computer functions are co-ordinated by this unit, which interprets and carries out the instructions contained in a program.

2 *Immediate access (or main) store*
   This consists of a very fast access store. Since the operation is electronic and there are no moving parts, data can be read in *nanoseconds* (one thousand millionths of a second).

3 *Arithmetic Unit*
   This is the operational unit. Here calculations are performed and the logical processes of selecting, sorting and comparing of information take place.

4 *Registers*
   These are small stores. They hold the data to be worked on in a calculation and give it up as instructed. Data can be transferred from one register to another.

Input Unit
   This reads the information to be stored in the machine and converts it into an electrical form which can later be used in arithmetical calculations.

Backing Store
   Data (information) can be permanently stored away here, usually in the form of recordings on magnetic material. It contains the vast mass of data a computer can deal with.

Output Unit
   This presents the results of a computer operation, often in printed form as on a payslip. It may be presented on a television screen, tape, disc, cassette or card.

12

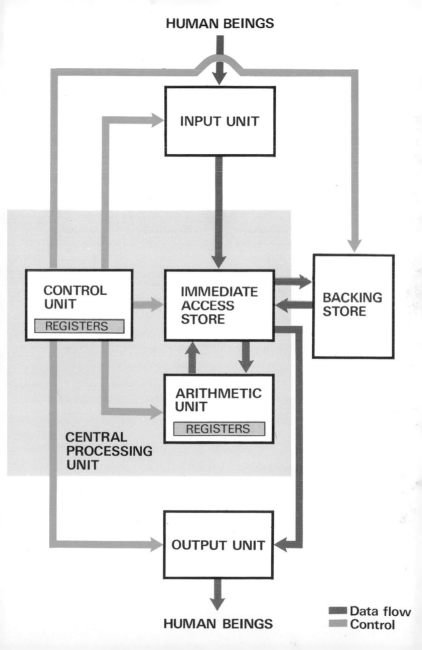

Combining the Parts

The main store, the arithmetic unit, and the control unit together with a group of registers, form what is called the *central processor*. Surrounding the central processor we have the input and output units together with the backing store. These are known as the *peripheral units*. Some peripherals can provide both input and output, such as Visual Display Units (VDUs).

We can now see in a very general way the method by which the computer works. Information in a specially prepared form is fed into the input unit where it is 'read' by a device which turns it into a series of electrical pulses. The computer then 'writes' down this information, that is, transfers it to a storage unit. The information that is stored is of two kinds: data, and instructions.

A list of instructions forms a *program*, and when the program is started, data is transferred into the arithmetic unit and calculations are carried out at a very high speed. All activities within the computer are supervised by the control unit.

The central processor is made up from several thousand transistors, together with other electrical components. Peripheral units are usually electrically-driven, mechanical devices.

INPUT

Card Reader

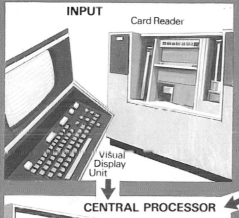

Visual Display Unit

MEMORY

Magnetic Tape Unit

Magnetic Disc Unit

CENTRAL PROCESSOR

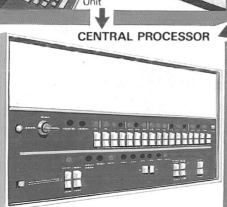

OUTPUT

Line Printer

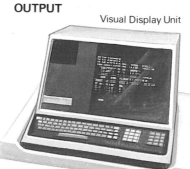

Visual Display Unit

The Computer Code

Human beings are able to recognise each other's handwriting and read the information that is written. They can also understand the spoken word. Different computers accept different input methods and different codes, just as humans speak and write in different languages. Since a computer has no brain, it must have the information fed into it in a particular way – by a code.

The more commonly-used methods of inputting code to a computer are VDU, punched card, magnetic tape, paper tape and document readers. Cards and paper tape have small holes punched through them in specially arranged patterns, down a column of a card or across the width of paper tape. These holes represent a given character, that is, a letter or a number.

Magnetic tapes and discs can be written from a device similar to a standard typewriter.

Document readers enable computers to 'read' information which is understandable to human beings. Common examples of these are electricity accounts and cheques. The characters on electricity billing documents can also be written by hand and 'read' into the computer. Bank cheques are preprinted with characters written in magnetic ink. Another example of code that can be read by human beings is that used by the VDU.

Pay
Two hundred & forty...
35p
Barclay & Fry Ltd

Will

⑈564028⑈ 20⑈5269⑆ 50526976⑈

MAGNETIC INK CHARACTERS

L4. MULTIPLY UNIT-COST BY QUANTITY GIVI

| PAGE | SERIAL | – | A | | B | | | | COBOL STATEMENT |

| PAGE | SERIAL | – | A | | B | | | | COBOL STATEMENT |

```
0-0 0 0 0 0 0 0 0 0 0 0 0 0 0 0 0 0 0 0 0 0 0 0 0 0 0 0 0 0 0 0 0 0 0 0
 1  2  3  4  5  6  7  8  9 10 11 12 13 14 15 16 17 18 19 20 21 22 23 24 25 26 27 28 29 30 31 32 33 34 35 36 37 38 39 40 41 42 43 44 45 46
1 1 1 1 1 1 1 1 1 1 1 1 1 1 1 1 1 1 1 1 1 1 1 1 1 1 1 1 1 1 1 1 1 1 1 1
2 2 2 2 2 2 2 2 2 2 2 2 2 2 2 2 2 2 2 2 2 2 2 2 2 2 2 2 2 2 2 2 2 2 2 2
3 3 3 3 3 3 3 3 3 3 3 3 3 3 3 3 3 3 3 3 3 3 3 3 3 3 3 3 3 3 3 3 3 3 3 3
4 4 4 4 4 4 4 4 4 4 4 4 4 4 4 4
```

COBOL SOURCE PROG

```
5 5 5 5 5 5 5 5 5 5 5 5 5 5 5 5 5 5 5 5 5 5 5 5 5 5 5 5 5 5 5 5 5 5 5 5
6 6 6 6 6 6 6 6 6 6 6 6 6 6 6 6 6 6 6 6 6 6 6 6 6 6 6 6 6 6 6 6 6 6 6 6
7 7 7 7 7 7 7 7 7 7 7 7 7 7 7 7 7 7 7 7 7 7 7 7 7 7 7 7 7 7 7 7 7 7 7 7
8 8 8 8 8 8 8 8 8 8 8 8 8 8 8 8 8 8 8 8 8 8 8 8 8 8 8 8 8 8 8 8 8 8 8 8
9 9 9 9 9 9 9 9 9 9 9 9 9 9 9 9 9 9 9 9 9 9 9 9 9 9 9 9 9 9 9 9 9 9 9 9
 5  6  7  8  9 10 11 12 13 14 15 16 17 18 19 20 21 22 23 24 25 26 27 28 29 30 31 32 33 34 35 36 37 38 39 40 41 42 43 44 45 46
```

IBM C61897

IBM

PUNCHED CARD

PUNCHED TAPE

The Input Unit

Cards or paper tape with their punched holes are placed in the input unit of the computer. Here, the computer's reading mechanism translates the patterns of holes into electrical pulses.

The cards are read at speeds around 1,000 cards per minute, and paper tape at around 1,000 characters per second. As the processing speeds are measured in nanoseconds (one thousand millionths of a second) these are both termed slow input devices. The reading may be done with light which shines through the holes and strikes a layer of photo-electric cells which turn the light dots into electrical pulses. Or cards can be passed between a roller conducting electricity and a series of tiny wire contacts. Where the holes appear the contacts momentarily touch the conductor and an electrical pulse is flashed into the machine. Where there is no hole there will, of course, be no electrical pulse produced; thus the coded pattern is turned into a series of pulses and no-pulses.

Document readers, or character recognition systems, can use photo-electric sensing on the shape of a written character as in electricity accounts. On cheques the magnetic pattern of the character is detected. These systems do not allow direct input into the computer but they do give an accurate method of reading data. They are first punched by an operator using a keyboard similar to that of an ordinary typewriter.

Visual Display Units (VDUs) are also important input devices. The keyboards to VDUs are similar to those of typewriters, and data input can be displayed on the screen. This method of reading data is used at Ladybird Books to check and record orders for books.

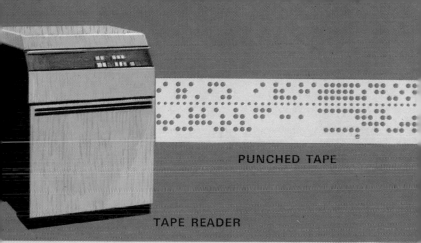

PUNCHED TAPE

TAPE READER

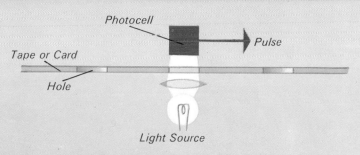

READING THE TAPE OR CARD

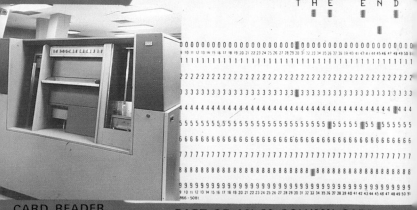

CARD READER

PART OF AN 80 COLUMN CARD

Recording Information on Magnetic Surfaces

Feeding information into the computer by means of cards and documents are well tried methods. Other materials increasingly employed are magnetic tapes, cassettes and diskettes (small flexible discs similar in size to a single gramophone record).

Magnetic devices have several advantages: they are much stronger than paper, the information can be packed in very tightly and is more easily removed, and the material is better to handle than either cards or paper. Perhaps one of the greatest advantages is that data can be changed or deleted using the same tape or diskette.

On the cassette illustrated opposite, the information is recorded in the form of magnetic spots which are arranged in patterns representing characters. When the cassette is read, its surface comes into contact with the reading/writing heads, a series of tiny coils, with which information can be recorded (written) or played back (read).

On a diskette the recording method is similar except that it is recorded onto many concentric circles, called tracks, across the faces of the diskette. Sometimes one side of the diskette is used, whilst for other equipment both sides of the diskette are used for recording information.

(See page 42 for more information.)

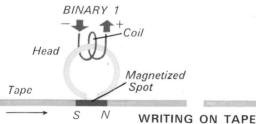

BINARY 1

Head

Coil

Tape

Magnetized Spot

S N **WRITING ON TAPE**

A current is passed through the coil of the head, which magnetizes a spot on the tape. A '1' has been written.

BINARY 0

N S

The direction of current flow is reversed which in turn reverses the polarity of the spot. A '0' (zero) has been written.

BINARY 1

S N **READING THE TAPE**

BINARY 0

N S

When the magnetized spot passes the 'read' head a voltage is induced in its coil, in one direction or the other. Thus a '1' or '0' is read.

Operation of Magnetic Tape Unit

Magnetic tape can be used for input, output or for storing data. It can carry up to a maximum of nine rows of magnetic spots, each row, or track, having its own reading/writing heads for playing back or recording the information. The tape is run from one reel onto another, not continuously, but as the information is required for processing within the computer. It is therefore important that an accurate stop/start arrangement is provided, and this is usually done by means of a constantly-rotating drive capstan and a pivoting pinch roller (see illustration). The tape cannot be read or written on until it has reached full running speed. For this reason, the information is not written in one long, continuous stream but in blocks, with a space between each block to allow a stopping and starting interval. This space, known as the inter-block gap, is approximately one inch long.

The tape driving motors are electrically operated and have very precise arrangements to ensure that the tape runs at a constant speed and that it can be started and stopped in an extremely short time. Actually, an acceleration from one inch per second to the normal running speed of seventy-five inches per second is usually accomplished in as little as two or three thousandths of a second. Slowing down and stopping takes the same time.

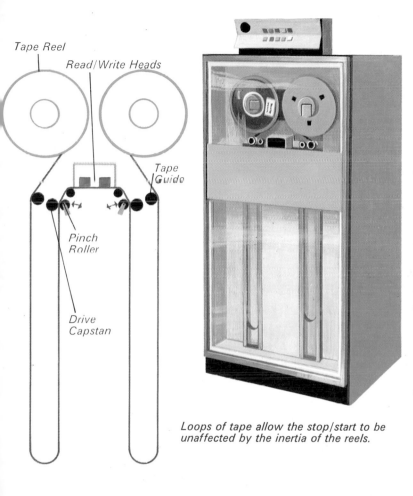

Tape Reel

Read/Write Heads

Tape Guide

Pinch Roller

Drive Capstan

Loops of tape allow the stop/start to be unaffected by the inertia of the reels.

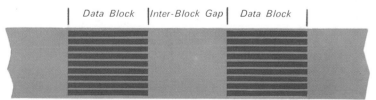

| Data Block | Inter-Block Gap | Data Block |

9 TRACK MAGNETIC TAPE

'Writing the Code'

Electrical pulses produced by the reading mechanism of the computer are next 'written down' – not with pen or pencil as we normally understand writing, but electrically. That is to say, the information represented by the pulses is recorded and held in a register or electrical store until it is needed for a calculation or other purpose. In a way this is rather like the human memory in which information is stored up ready to be brought forward when it is required.

We have seen that a suitable code for a digital computer uses only two pieces of information, namely a 'pulse' or 'no-pulse'. Such information is called *binary* (see page 36) and can be represented by numbers. For example, 'pulse' = 1, 'no-pulse' = 0.

The diagram on the page opposite illustrates how such information can be transferred from the reading mechanism to a register. A *shift register* is shown – so called because the arrival of the first pulse (or no-pulse) causes the information already stored to move one place to the right (in this case the register was initially empty). A vacant position occurs at the extreme left-hand end and the pulse which triggered the move right is stored there. The process is repeated each time a pulse (or no-pulse) arrives, until the whole register is full.

We already know that 'reading' is taking the coded information from punched cards or paper tape. 'Writing' is recording this information and storing it away for future use.

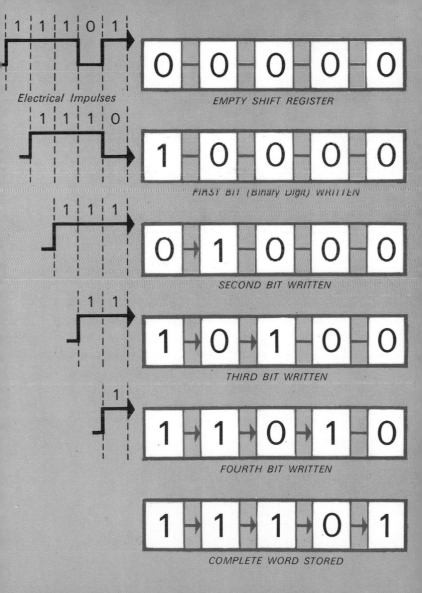

Electrical Impulses

EMPTY SHIFT REGISTER

FIRST BIT (Binary Digit) WRITTEN

SECOND BIT WRITTEN

THIRD BIT WRITTEN

FOURTH BIT WRITTEN

COMPLETE WORD STORED

THE WORD '11101' WRITTEN AND STORED IN A SHIFT REGISTER

The Computer Store

Human beings cannot remember everything that enters their brains and their general knowledge is limited. But they are able to refer to books of various kinds to find the information they need. These books are stores of information, often contained in a library where they can be referred to from time to time.

One of the most important features of a modern computer system is its ability to hold a vast amount of information which can be drawn upon when required. The registers, we know, are small working stores used mostly for arithmetic calculations and have a very limited capacity for storing information. It is therefore necessary to have an extra storage system where alpha numeric information can be held more permanently. The information can be produced, like a book in a library, for processing in the registers, and returned to the store when finished with. Out-of-date information can be removed and new data added.

There are several types of storage systems in use, most of them magnetic, and we shall be dealing with these in the next few chapters. They each have advantages and disadvantages. Some are more efficient but too expensive for many computer applications. Some have extra large capacity; others are very fast. Generally speaking, computer stores are a compromise between speed, convenience and expense.

MAGNETIC TAPE UNIT

MAGNETIC DISC UNIT

'Words', 'Bits', and 'Addresses'

A computer word is an arrangement of binary digits, or *bits*, which have a special meaning to the computer. The number of bits needed to form a single character is called a *byte*. The number of bits in a word is known as the *word length* and may be as many as fifty, although this figure will vary according to the design of the computer.

The store of the central processor can contain several million words. Most computer systems have between 16 and 256 thousand words capacity, but this is constantly increasing. It is necessary to select a certain number of these words for use in a particular calculation. It is vitally important, therefore, that their exact positions are known, otherwise the calculation could not take place. The store is, in fact, divided up into compartments, or *locations*. Each location holds a word and its position is identified by a serial number known as the *address*.

Computer words are of two types: *instruction words* which tell the computer what to do, and *data words* which represent the numbers the computer has to use in its calculations. An instruction word has itself got two parts: the first part is the operation code, or op. code, which describes in number form the operation to be performed. The second part contains one or more addresses of data words with which the computer is to carry out its arithmetic. The number of addresses required for a particular calculation may vary between one and three but is more usually one or two. The tables opposite show how information may be contained in instruction words for the different systems.

INSTRUCTION

Operation Code	Address 1	Address 2	Address 3

←———————— 1 word ————————→

THREE-ADDRESS SYSTEM

OP. CODE	The operation to be executed by the computer
ADDRESS 1	The address of the first piece of data
ADDRESS 2	The address of the second piece of data
ADDRESS 3	The address into which result should be placed

TWO-ADDRESS SYSTEM

OP. CODE	The operation to be executed by the computer
ADDRESS 1	The address of the first piece of data
ADDRESS 2	The address of the second piece of data

ONE-ADDRESS SYSTEM

OP. CODE	The operation to be executed by the computer
ADDRESS	The address of the data

The Magnetic Core Store

The calculating speed of a computer depends on the time needed to select and take two numbers from a store and return the result of the calculation to it. What we must therefore have is the fastest possible access time.

A widely-used type of high-speed store, particularly for the computer's central processor, employs *ferrite* rings. These are very small rings of a ceramic material which can be magnetized. Each ring, about the size of a typewriter 'full stop', is known as a core and is capable of being magnetized in one of two states in order to represent either a binary 1 or 0. The cores are threaded onto wire grids at the point where the wires cross. The change from one state to the other of any one core — called *switching* — can only be brought about by passing a pulse of current along each of the two wires which link that core uniquely. A third wire — called the sense wire — is used to read the information stored.

Any word in the store can be reached in an equal time. For this reason magnetic core stores are often known as equal time stores (they are also referred to as random access stores), and computers using them are able to make over a hundred million additions every second. Present-day stores are etched onto silicon chips; the method of reading and writing these is similar to that of the ferrite core. These electronic cores are called MOS (Metal Oxide Semi-conductors).

Ferrite Ring or Core

(a)   (b)   (c)

MAGNETIZING A CORE

(a) A pulse of current magnetizes the core. Binary 1 is written.
(b) When the pulse is removed the magnetism remains.
(c) A pulse in the opposite direction reverses the core's magnetic state.
    Binary 0 is written.

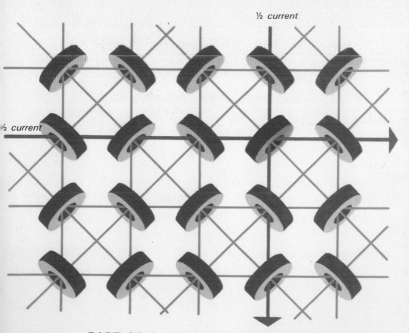

½ current

½ current

PART OF A MAGNETIC CORE STORE

Half of the current needed to switch a core is passed through a horizontal and a vertical wire, only the core at the intersection of the wires receiving the full current. By this means any core may be switched without affecting the remainder. The diagonal 'sense' wires are used when reading.

'Gates' and 'Highways'

To understand how a computer works when moving numbers around the central processor, we must try to think in terms of short electrical pulses, each lasting for about one millionth of a second and following each other like bullets out of a machine gun, but many thousands of times faster. The wires along which the pulses travel between one register and another are known as *highways* and the electronic switches which can be opened to admit a pulse, or closed to block it off, are known as *gates*.

Numbers, represented by the pattern of pulses and no-pulses, are sent speeding along the highways, and the appropriate gates are opened or closed as necessary to admit them or block them off. For example, in the diagram opposite, numbers from any two of the three registers, A, B, and C, can be sent down the highways leading to the adder and the resulting sum returned to A, B, and C.

This example shows that by controlling the time for which a group of gates is opened it is possible to form many different routes in the computer in a fraction of a second. The calculating speed of a computer is determined both by the speed at which information can be selected from the various locations and by the speed with which the routes can be set up.

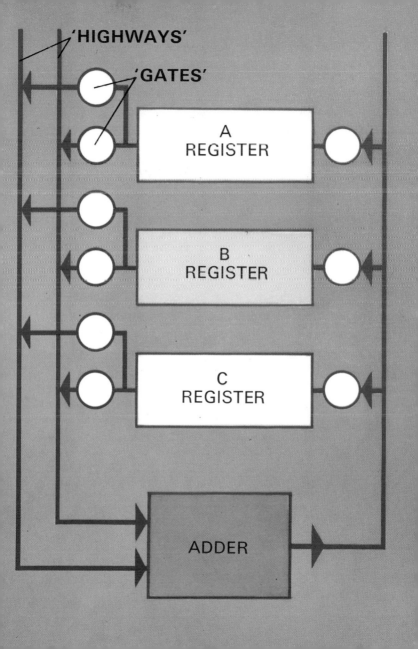

Computer Arithmetic

The electronic circuits used in a computer are arranged so that the coded pattern on the input cards or tape can be used to perform arithmetic – done in a special unit called the *arithmetic unit*. Before describing how it does this, let us see what sort of arithmetic we require the computer to do. It is possible to perform very long and complicated calculations by breaking them down into a number of simple calculations strung together in the right order to give the final answer. Addition, subtraction, multiplication and division are the arithmetic operations used most frequently, and so the arithmetic unit is designed to do just these.

Those readers who have seen or used a hand calculating machine will remember that turning the handle clockwise adds the number in one register to the contents of another, while turning it anti-clockwise subtracts one number from another. Numbers in a register can also be shifted to the left or to the right by means of another handle. In this way multiplication and division can be performed. The circuits in the arithmetic unit do the same job but work, of course, very many times faster than our hand calculating machine.

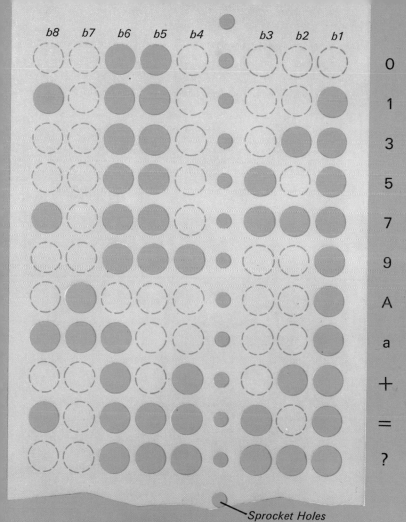

Diagram showing how NUMERIC and ALPHABETIC data is coded on 8-hole punched paper tape before entering the store and being used in the ARITHMETIC UNIT.

pulse

no pulse

Binary Arithmetic

We have seen that information travels along the highways as pulses or no-pulses. If we call each of these a digit, then the arithmetic unit has to do its arithmetic with only two digits instead of the ten that we use for our own calculations. The system using ten digits is the decimal system, the system using only two digits is called the *binary* system. The numbers used in the binary system are 0 and 1, so that a pulse can represent a 1 and a no-pulse a 0 (equally well the reverse would be true but will not be used).

The examples at the top of the page opposite show how the two number systems are made up. Those students who already have some knowledge of arithmetic will know that addition and subtraction follow fixed rules and that two tables can be built up, one for addition and one for subtraction, which will give the answer for any two digits which we wish to add or subtract. For binary arithmetic there are four entries in each table, as shown opposite. Keeping an eye on these tables will help when following the examples given of binary addition and subtraction.

EXAMPLES OF COMPUTER ARITHMETIC

A Decimal number is written:

$$\boxed{5638} \equiv \boxed{5 \times 1000} + \boxed{6 \times 100} + \boxed{3 \times 10} + \boxed{8 \times 1}$$

$$\equiv \boxed{5 \times 10^3} + \boxed{6 \times 10^2} + \boxed{3 \times 10^1} + \boxed{8 \times 10^0}$$

A Binary number is written:

$$\boxed{1101} \equiv \boxed{1 \times 2^3} + \boxed{1 \times 2^2} + \boxed{0 \times 2^1} + \boxed{1 \times 2^0}$$

$$\equiv \boxed{1 \times 8} + \boxed{1 \times 4} + \boxed{0 \times 2} + \boxed{1 \times 1}$$

$$\equiv \boxed{13 \text{ as a decimal number}}$$

Knowing how to translate from Binary to Decimal, together with the tables for addition and subtraction, we can work some examples.

ADDITION TABLE		
	+0	+1
+0	0	1
+1	1	0 + carry 1

SUBTRACTION TABLE		
	+1	+0
−0	1	0
−1	0	1 + borrow 1

```
                c  c
                ↶  ↶
       7       0 1 1 1
     + 6     + 0 1 1 0
    ─────    ─────────
      13       1 1 0 1
```

```
                b  b
                ↷  ↷
      13       1 1 0 1
     − 7     − 0 1 1 1
    ─────    ─────────
       6       0 1 1 0
```

Programming

A set of instructions given to a computer is known as a *program*. The first step in preparing such a program is to draw a flow chart, two examples of which are shown opposite. This is built up from a number of connected boxes, the label attached to each box showing the job or calculation which is to be done at each step. One very important type of box is the decision box, in which a question is asked. The only answers allowed to the computer are 'yes' or 'no' and although this may seem too simple to be of use in a complicated problem, remember that a computer can ask nearly half a million questions a second!

Transferring the job of each box into number form (*machine code*) is very laborious, and the programmer is helped in this task by an intermediate language (*high level language*) which is then translated by a master program (*the compiler*) into machine code. There are many high level languages in use, the most common being COBOL (COmmon Business Orientated Language), BASIC (Beginners All-purpose Symbolic Instruction Code), PL1 (Programming Language One), FORTRAN (FORmula TRANslation), and RPG (Report Program Generator).

Programming in machine code is a job for a highly-trained person, whereas programming in a high level language is something many people can do provided they are given time to learn the rules that must be followed.

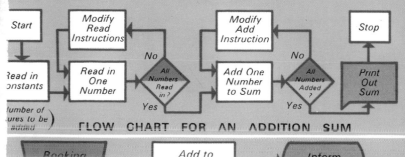

FLOW CHART FOR AN ADDITION SUM

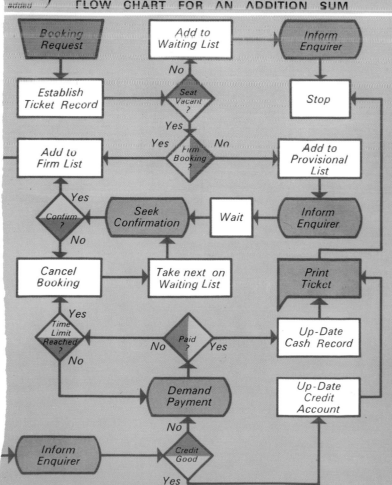

FLOW CHART FOR A FLIGHT BOOKING

The Control Unit

We have seen that a program is a list of instructions kept in the store of a computer. To make this program work, the computer has to look at each instruction in turn and find out what it means. When it has done this the calculation, or *data movement*, can be carried out. To see the steps involved, look at the diagram opposite.

An *instruction* is fetched from the store and kept temporarily in a register in the *control unit*. Both the *operation* to be carried out and the *address* of the data on which the operation is to be made can then be found. The correct sequence of control signals for this code are produced and sent to the gates; these cause the calculation or data movement to take place. The time at which each control signal is sent is carefully controlled by the computer 'clock', which sends out a continuous string of pulses, so keeping all the data movements in step with each other. Meanwhile, the address of the next instruction to be fetched is found by adding +1 to the address of the instruction which has just been used. The process then repeats itself, with instructions being first 'analysed', then 'executed' in sequence, until the program is complete.

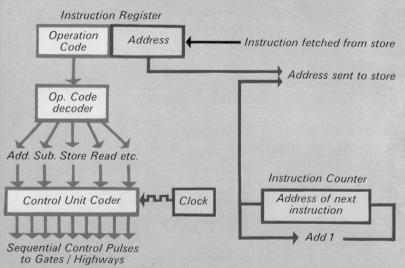

Instruction Register

| Operation Code | Address | ← *Instruction fetched from store* |

→ *Address sent to store*

Op. Code decoder

Add. Sub. Store Read etc.

Control Unit Coder ⟿ *Clock*

Sequential Control Pulses to Gates / Highways

Instruction Counter

Address of next instruction

→ *Add 1*

PRINCIPLE OF COMPUTER CONTROL UNIT

The Disc Store

Most computer systems these days are provided with a direct access store in addition to the random access core storage. It provides a very large backing store for information that is not in constant use and therefore does not need quite such a short access time.

Some smaller computers use the magnetic diskette system for random access but in the bigger installations a disc store is more likely to be employed. This consists of one or more metal discs which continuously rotate on a spindle. The flat surface of each disc is covered with closely-packed, concentric tracks of magnetic spots − similar to the grooves on a gramophone record − and they are read or written on by reading/writing heads, mounted on arms which can move radially across the disc to select the required track. Disc stores may have a capacity of five hundred million words and an access time of around thirty one thousandths of a second. These capacity and access times are constantly being improved.

A cheaper form of random access store uses magnetic stripe cards. These are bigger than punched cards and they are packed into magazine-type containers. Any card can be taken from a magazine and passed over a reading/writing head before being returned to the magazine. The capacity of a card store may be five thousand words.

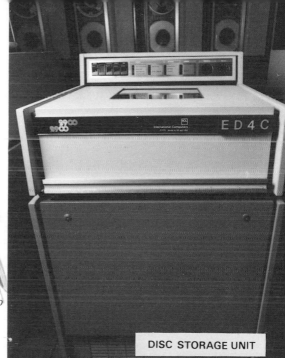

ED4C

Loading a disc pack into the unit.

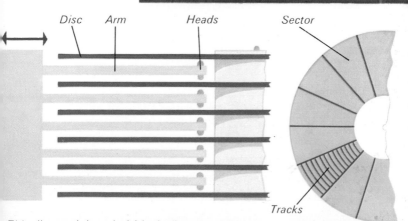

Disc   Arm   Heads   Sector

Tracks

This disc pack has six 14 inch discs providing ten recording surfaces.
The arm assembly moves in and out to give the heads access to the whole
recording area. Data address specifies disc, sector and track.

The Output Unit

The final part of a computer is the output unit, which presents the results of the machine's operations in printed or other visual form, or on tapes and discs.

One type of printer is able to print a complete line at a time. Briefly, it consists of a series of 132 revolving wheels which have spaced around their circumference all the letters of the alphabet as well as the decimal numbers. Paper is placed over the type-wheels with a printer ribbon between. As the correct characters come into position, a row of electrically-operated hammers strike the paper which then takes an impression of the type.

Another method uses a process known as Xerography in which tiny specks of powdered ink are electrostatically drawn towards plastic-coated paper. An electrical pulse is passed through the line of type to be printed and this collects the specks together into the shape of the various characters. The print is then 'fixed' by passing through heated rollers which soften the plastic coating.

Still another way we can get output, including graphs and drawings, is a display on a VDU. The Visual Display Unit shown opposite is a combined input/output device. The operator can communicate with the computer by means of the keyboard or by using a 'light pen' on the tube face. The VDU can also display reports in the form of text, such as a list of employees.

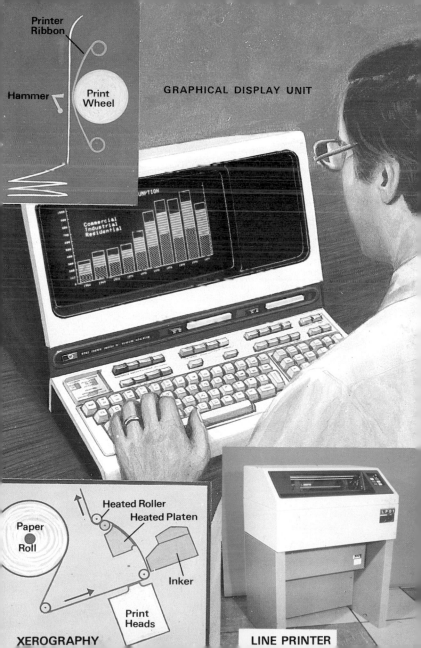

Printer Ribbon

Hammer

Print Wheel

GRAPHICAL DISPLAY UNIT

XEROGRAPHY

Paper Roll

Heated Roller
Heated Platen

Inker

Print Heads

LINE PRINTER

Teleprocessing

When you go into a branch office of a large national company such as a travel agent or an insurance company, the questions you ask will probably be sent via a terminal to a control computer at the main office of the firm. The answers to your questions will then be returned and printed out at the branch office.

This is called *teleprocessing*, which means 'processing at a distance'. (The Greek prefix 'tele', meaning at a distance, can be seen in other words such as telescope, television and telephone.)

A computer system may be contained within a single building complex, or may spread across a continent, where information of national importance may be required.

To transmit data over such large distances, its form needs to be changed. This is accomplished by a *modem* – a Modulator/Demodulator which adds a powerful *carrier* wave to the data to enable it to travel down a telephone wire or as a radio wave. At the terminal end, the data is *modulated* (the carrier wave is added) for transmission, and at the receiving end it is *demodulated* (carrier wave is removed) for the computer to accept. As it is normal to have a question and answer system, the modulator and demodulator units are held in a single unit, the modem.

Frequency modulation and amplitude modulation are the simplest forms of modulation (*see* Ladybird Book – How it works: The Television). At various stages of transmission the data will be amplified to bring its strength up and pass it on to the next stage.

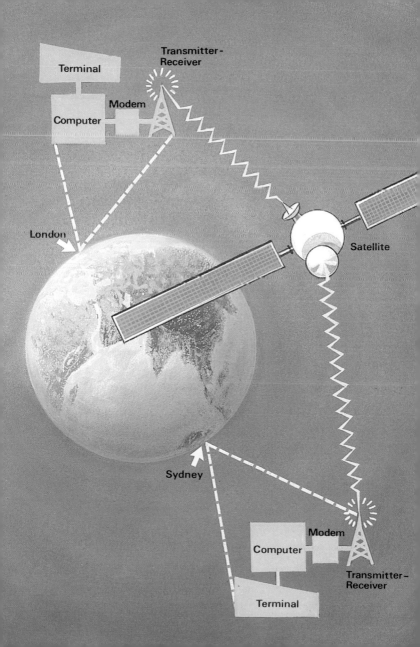

Terminal

Computer

Modem

Transmitter-Receiver

London

Satellite

Sydney

Computer

Modem

Transmitter-Receiver

Terminal

Does a Computer make Mistakes?

Programmers, being human, are always liable to make mistakes. Computers, being machines, occasionally develop some fault or other. Either way, the final result is not of much use.

Information to be fed into a computer can be checked by a second operator using a machine called a *verifier*. The original punched card (or tape) is put into the machine and, referring to the papers from which the first version was prepared, the checking operator tries to punch out a second version. If the first and second cards agree, the characters are punched out in a verified card. If they do not agree, the keyboard locks and the operator has to discover where the fault lies.

A programmer may make a mistake either in writing out the machine code or in a wrong analysis of the situation on which the program was based. Mistakes of this kind are very difficult to trace and the process of tracking them down is known as *debugging*.

Finally, there exists the possibility of a machine fault. In the input/output devices an additional digit can be added to the code in such a way that an error can be detected. Within the machine, faults can only be detected by running test programs which check each part of the computer.

VISUAL DISPLAY UNITS IN OPERATION

In one common method of error detection, used in computer storage systems, an extra digit, known as a 'parity bit' is added to each coded character. When the character being stored has an odd number of binary 1's a 1 is added. When it has an even number of 1's a 0 is added. Each time a character is read the number of 1's is sensed and compared with the parity bit. If they are unlike the error is indicated by an alarm.

CHARACTER	PARITY BIT
1101	1
0101	0
1001	1
error	

This Year, Next Year, Sometime . . . ?

The use of computers is growing year by year and their design is changing almost as quickly. What was up-to-date five years ago is out-of-date today and what is the latest thing today will be old-hat in five years' time.

Apart from their applications in offices, banks, the post office, engineering establishments, airlines and many other fields of operation, computers are now used to control the flight of a spacecraft, and to supervise the working of a machine-tool. In its commercial and scientific applications, information goes in through the input unit and the calculated result is presented on the output device. Operating in areas such as spacecraft and machine-tools, the computer is working in real time, that is, being used to control the actual movement of a vehicle or the cutting edge of a tool.

Computers themselves are continually changing. Electronic valves are no longer used and have been replaced by transistors and diodes which have a low current consumption, greater reliability and much smaller dimensions. Printed circuits and stores are consistently being reduced in physical size as more research into different materials takes place. Many thousands of components can now be fitted into silicon chips approximately one-third of a centimetre square. The future will see much more compact machines doing an even greater variety of intricate jobs.

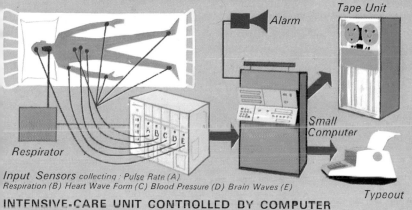

Input Sensors collecting : Pulse Rate (A)
Respiration (B) Heart Wave Form (C) Blood Pressure (D) Brain Waves (E)

INTENSIVE-CARE UNIT CONTROLLED BY COMPUTER
Patients body functions are monitored by the computer which sounds an alarm at any sign of danger.

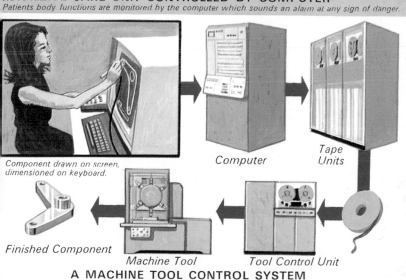

Component drawn on screen, dimensioned on keyboard.

Computer

Tape Units

Finished Component

Machine Tool

Tool Control Unit

A MACHINE TOOL CONTROL SYSTEM

A MICROPROCESSOR

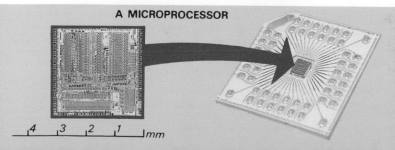

Glossary of Terms

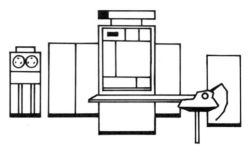

Computers, like many other things, have given rise to their own terminology or jargon, and it is important to distinguish the special meaning of such terms from any more common meaning they may have. The following glossary may, therefore, be helpful for reference.

ADDRESS   Computers store numbers and instructions in their store. The store is usually divided into locations each of which holds one number or instruction. Each of these locations is given a designation so that it can be referred to, no matter what number or instruction it happens to contain. This designation is often called the 'address' of the location.

CENTRAL PROCESSOR   That part of the computer which does all the calculating.

FLOW DIAGRAM   A diagram showing the essential steps in a calculation, in particular the various branches which may occur for different cases.